P9-BYJ-242

The AMAZING WORLD OF

GUMBALL™

RECIPE FOR DISASTER

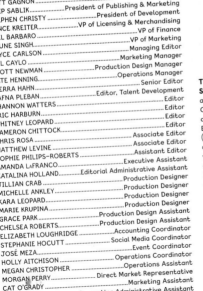

ROSS RICHIE ....CEO & Founder
MATT GAGNON ....Editor-in-Chief
FILIP SABLIK......................President of Publishing & Marketing
STEPHEN CHRISTY ....President of Development
LANCE KREITER............VP of Licensing & Merchandising
PHIL BARBARO ....VP of Finance
ARUNE SINGH ....VP of Marketing
BRYCE CARLSON ....Managing Editor
MEL CAYLO ....Marketing Manager
SCOTT NEWMAN ....Production Design Manager
KATE HENNING................................Operations Manager
SIERRA HAHN..Senior Editor
DAFNA PLEBAN ....Editor, Talent Development
SHANNON WATTERS ....Editor
ERIC HARBURN...Editor
WHITNEY LEOPARD ....Editor
CAMERON CHITTOCK...Editor
CHRIS ROSA ....Associate Editor
MATTHEW LEVINE ....Associate Editor
SOPHIE PHILIPS-ROBERTS ....Assistant Editor
AMANDA LaFRANCO.................................Executive Assistant
KATALINA HOLLAND...........Editorial Administrative Assistant
JILLIAN CRAB ....Production Designer
MICHELLE ANKLEY..................................Production Designer
KARA LEOPARD..Production Designer
MARIE KRUPINA................................Production Designer
GRACE PARK.............................Production Design Assistant
CHELSEA ROBERTS.................Production Design Assistant
ELIZABETH LOUGHRIDGE ....Accounting Coordinator
STEPHANIE HOCUTT ....Social Media Coordinator
JOSÉ MEZA..Event Coordinator
HOLLY AITCHISON ....Operations Coordinator
MEGAN CHRISTOPHER ....Operations Assistant
MORGAN PERRY.....................Direct Market Representative
CAT O'GRADY...Marketing Assistant
LIZ ALMENDAREZ.............Accounting Administrative Assistant
CORNELÍA TZANA ....Administrative Assistant

kaboom!™   CN CARTOON NETWORK.

THE AMAZING WORLD OF GUMBALL: RECIPE FOR DISASTER SCHOLASTIC EDITION, October 2017. Published by KaBOOM!, a division of Boom Entertainment, Inc. THE AMAZING WORLD OF GUMBALL, CARTOON NETWORK, the logos, and all related characters and elements are trademarks of and © Turner Broadcasting System Europe Limited. Cartoon Network. (S17) All rights reserved. KaBOOM!™ and the KaBOOM! logo are trademarks of Boom Entertainment, Inc., registered in various countries and categories. All characters, events, and institutions depicted herein are fictional. Any similarity between any of the names, characters, persons, events, and/or institutions in this publication to actual names, characters, and persons, whether living or dead, events, and/or institutions is unintended and purely coincidental. KaBOOM! does not read or accept unsolicited submissions of ideas, stories, or artwork.

For information regarding the CPSIA on this printed material, call: (203) 595-3636 and provide reference RICH # – 766328.

BOOM! Studios, 5670 Wilshire Boulevard, Suite 450, Los Angeles, CA 90036-5679. Printed in USA. Second Printing.

ISBN: 978-1-68415-158-5

The AMAZING WORLD OF GUMBALL™

RECIPE FOR DISASTER

created by **BEN BOCQUELET**

script by **MEGAN BRENNAN**
art by **KATY FARINA**
colors by **WHITNEY COGAR**
letters by **WARREN MONTGOMERY**

"A PIE FOR A PIE"
script & art by **KATE SHERRON**

cover by **KATY FARINA**

designer **JILLIAN CRAB**
assistant editors **MATTHEW LEVINE** and **MARY GUMPORT**
editor **SIERRA HAHN**

with special thanks to **MARISA MARIONAKIS, RICK BLANCO, JANET NO, CURTIS LELASH, CONRAD MONTGOMERY, MEGHAN BRADLEY** and the wonderful folks at **CARTOON NETWORK**.

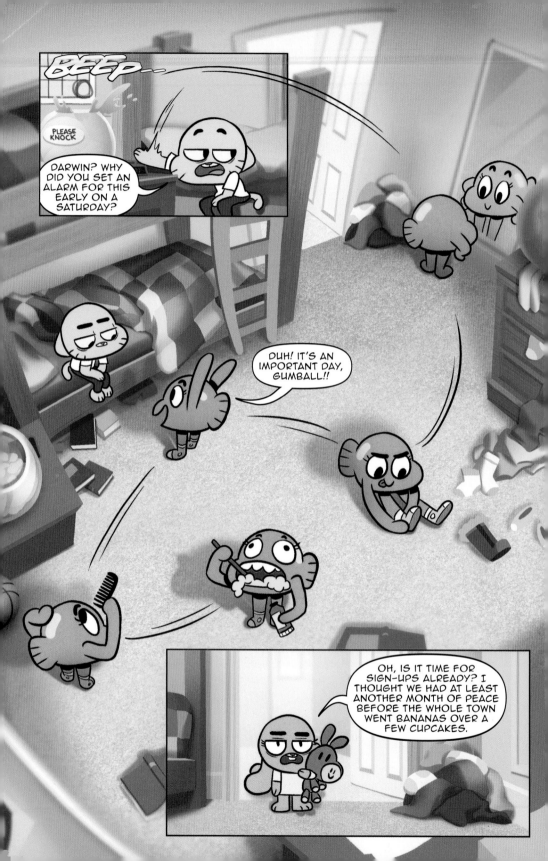

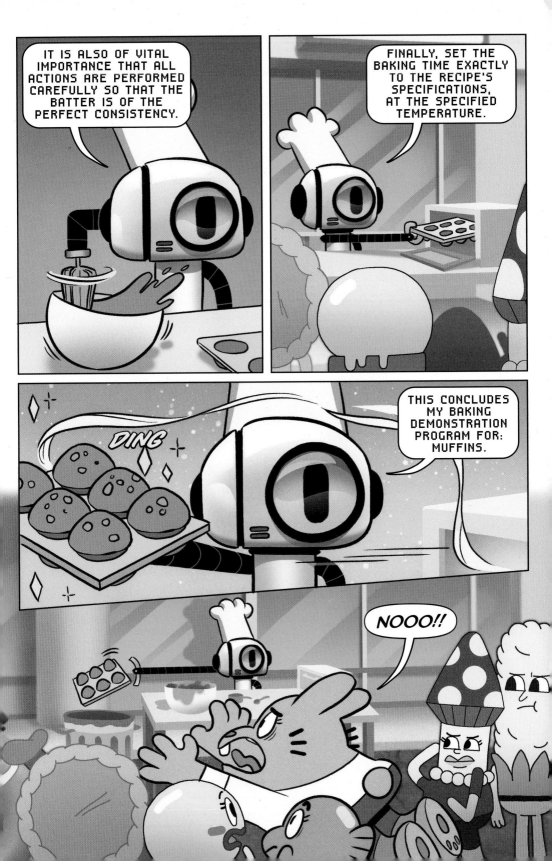

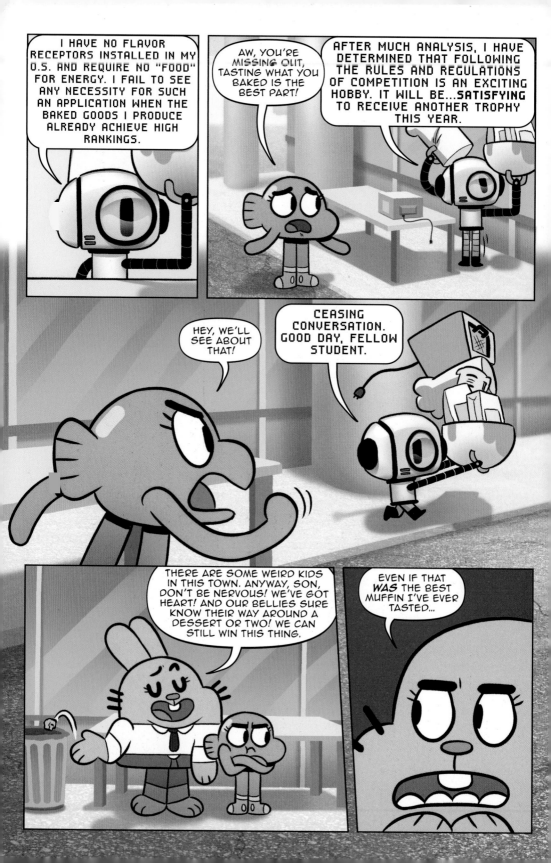

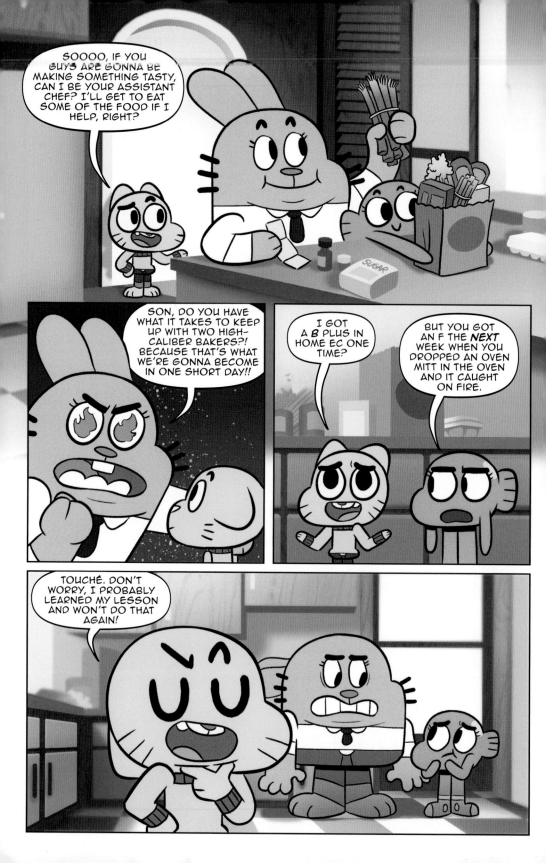

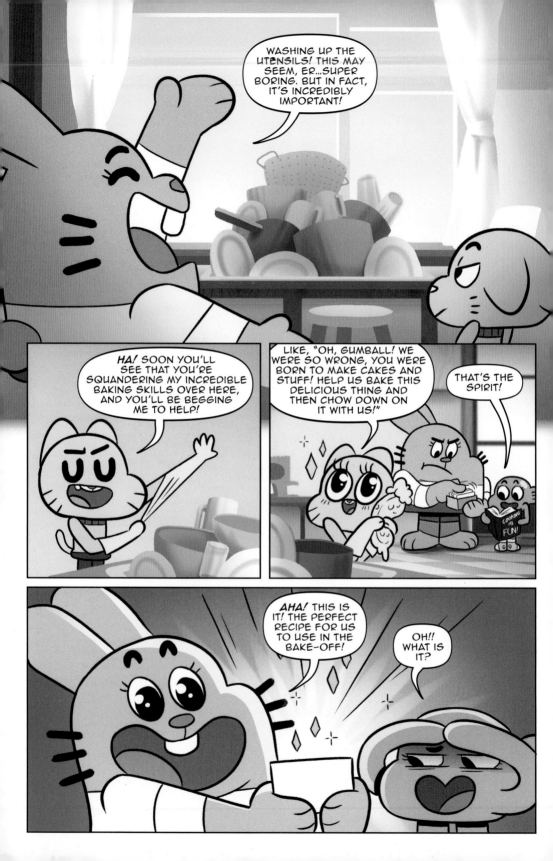

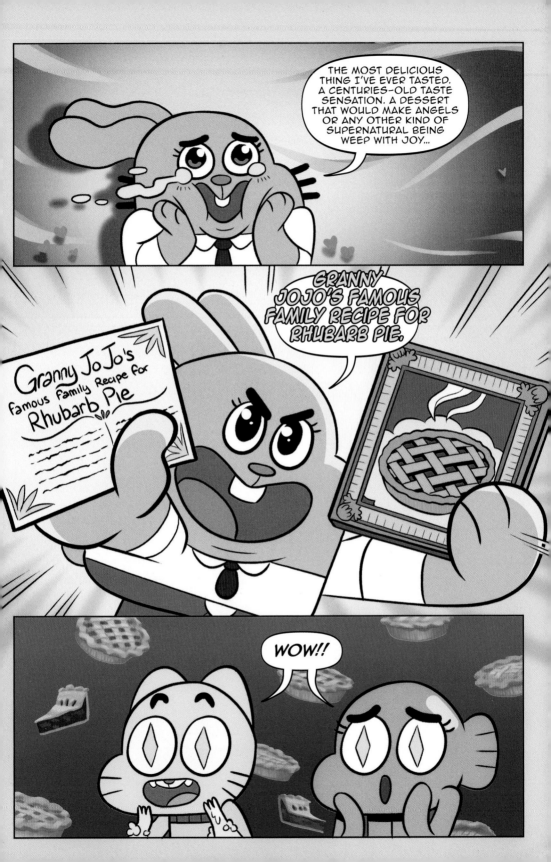

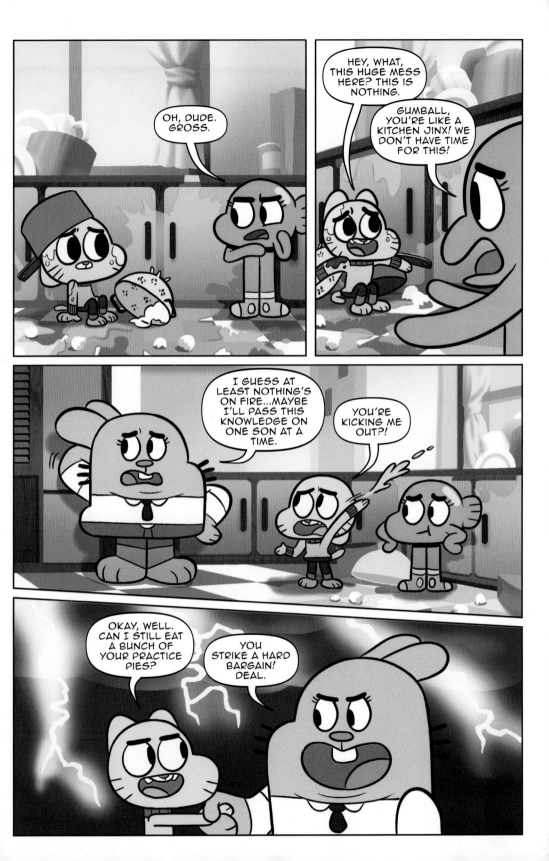

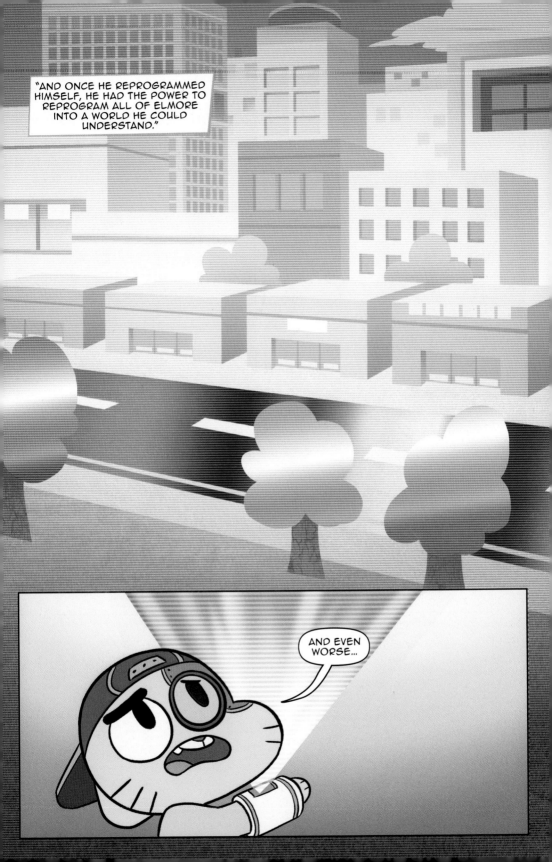

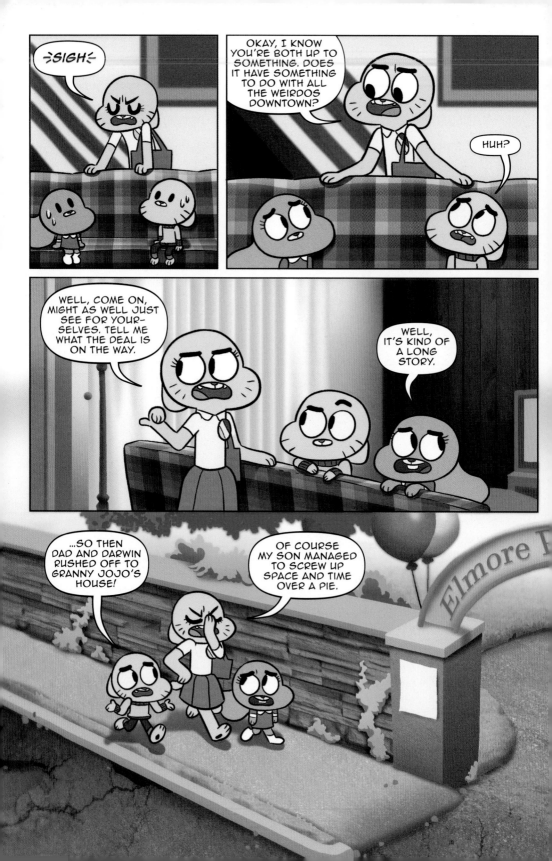

WE'VE GOTTA THINK OF A WAY TO STOP THEM FROM CLOGGING UP OUR REALITY! MAYBE WE COULD TRICK THEM INTO GETTING ON A SCHOOL BUS AND WE COULD DRIVE IT TO AN ABANDONED FIELD UNTIL THE BAKE-OFF ENDS--

OH, DON'T WORRY. I'VE GOT A PLAN.

HELLO? GRANNY JOJO?

I KNOW WHY YOU HAVE COME.

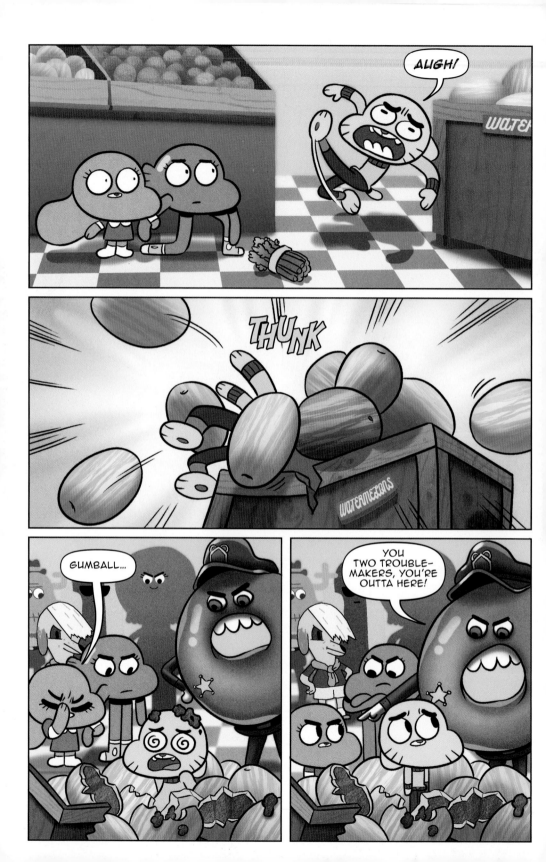

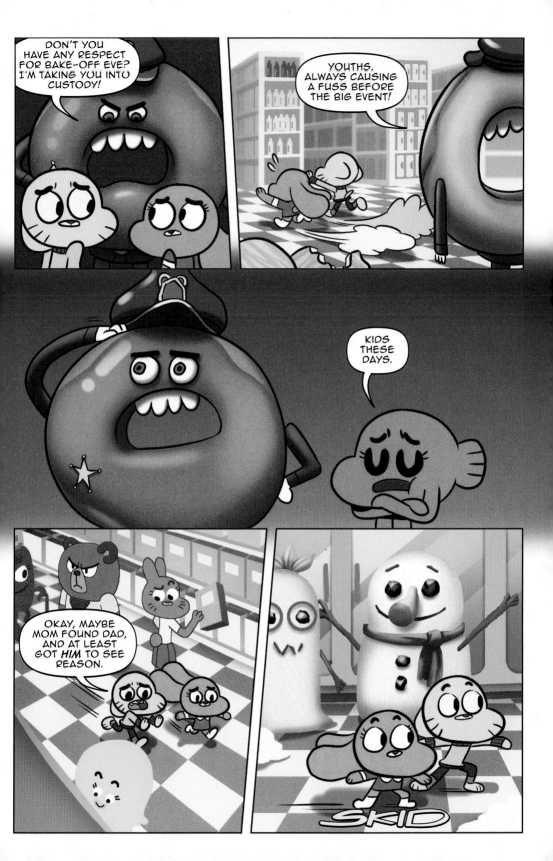

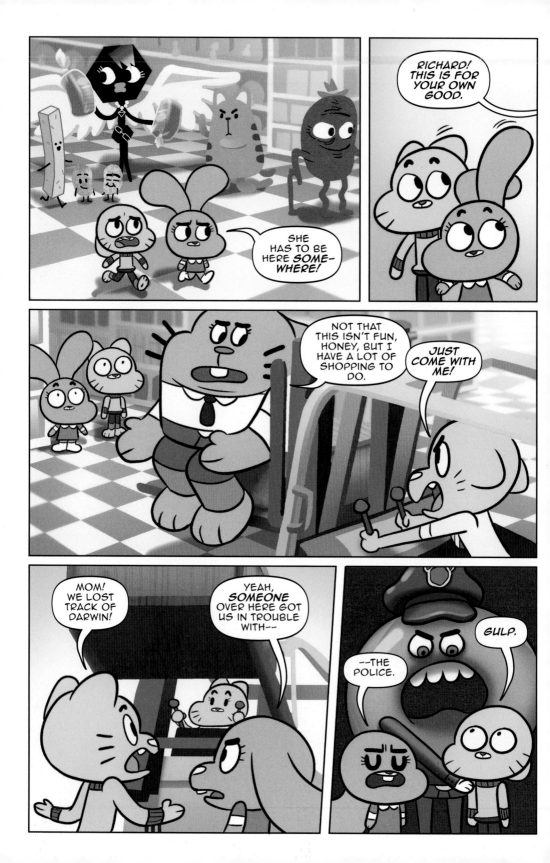

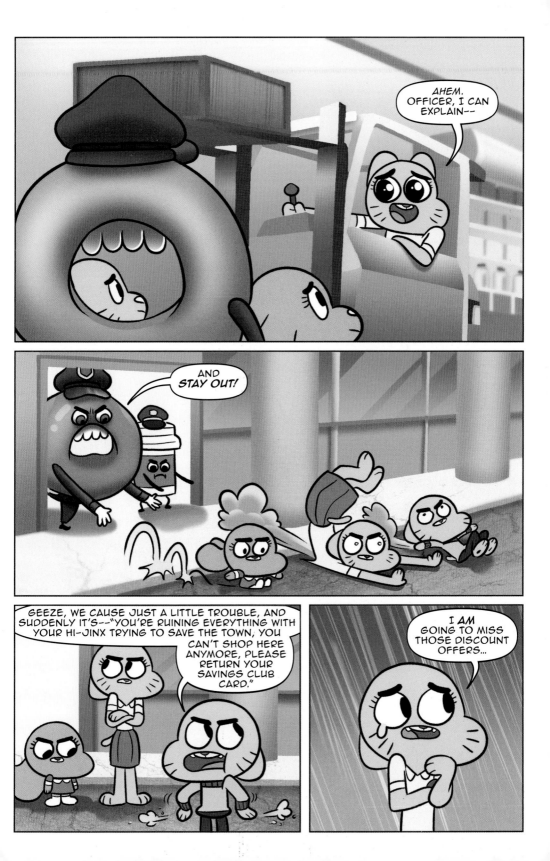

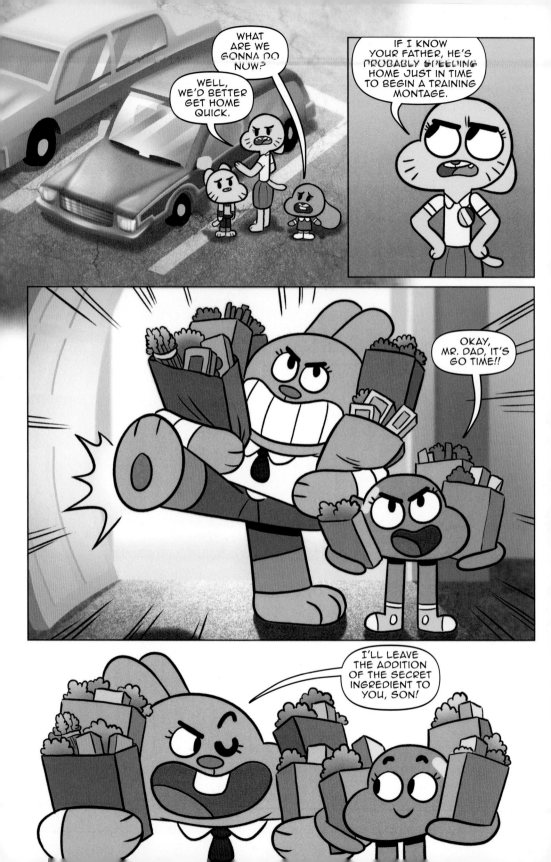

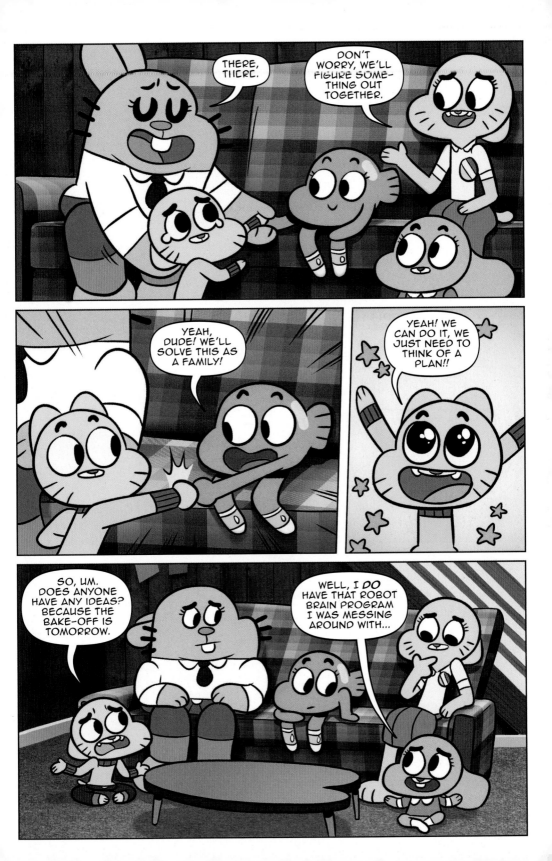

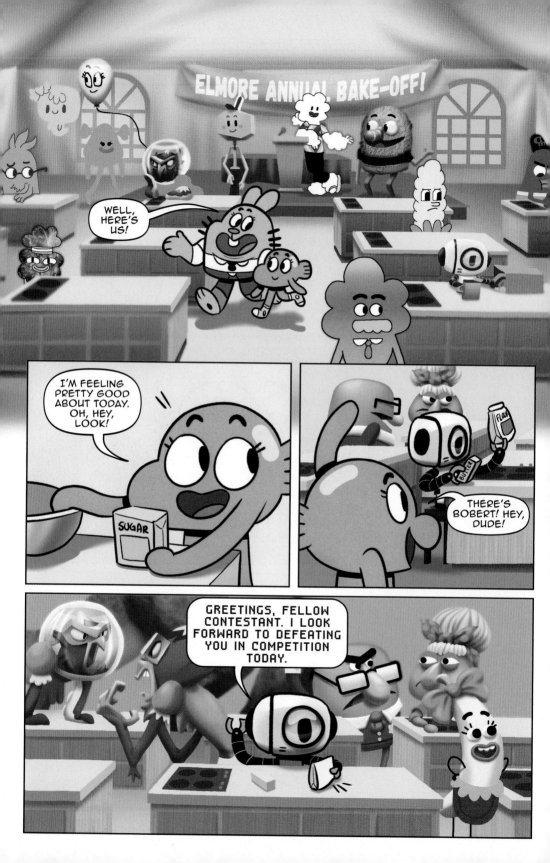

WELL, BLESS HIS HEART.

ELMORE ANNUAL BAKE-OFF!

AHEM. WELCOME, CONTESTANTS, TO THE *ELMORE ANNUAL BAKE-OFF!*

BAKERS, GET READY!

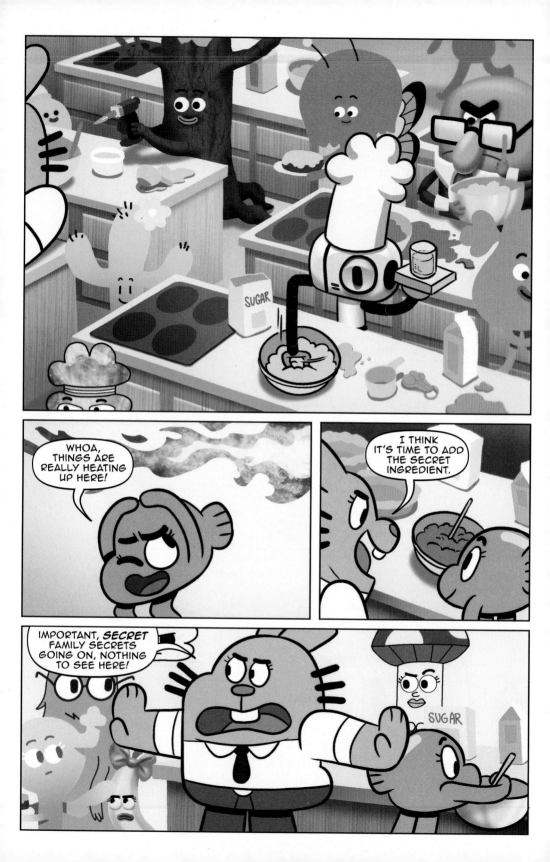

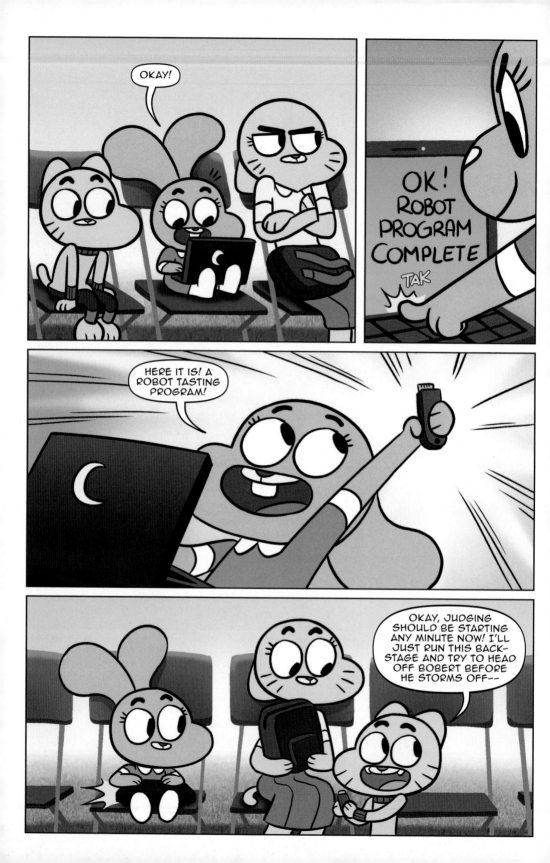

WELL, THERE IT GOES! OUR PRIDE AND JOY.

HEY, DON'T GIVE OUR PIE THAT LOOK! IT'S GONNA WIN BIG, JUST YOU WAIT!!

SOON WE WILL SEE WHO THE WINNER IS. MY CAKE WILL BE, AS THEY SAY, A SHOE-IN.

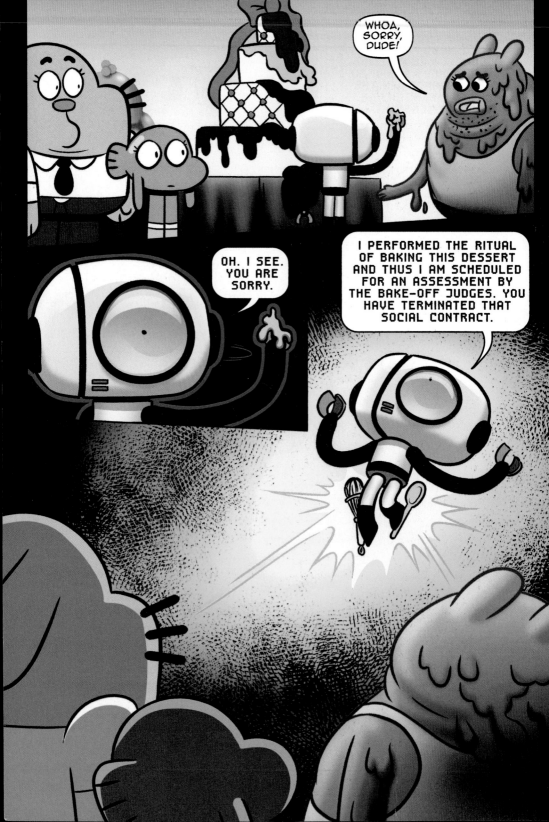

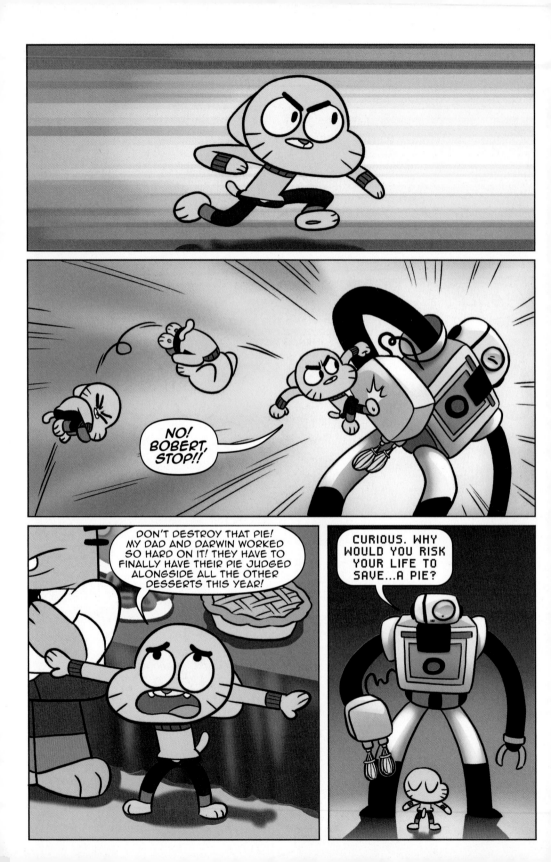

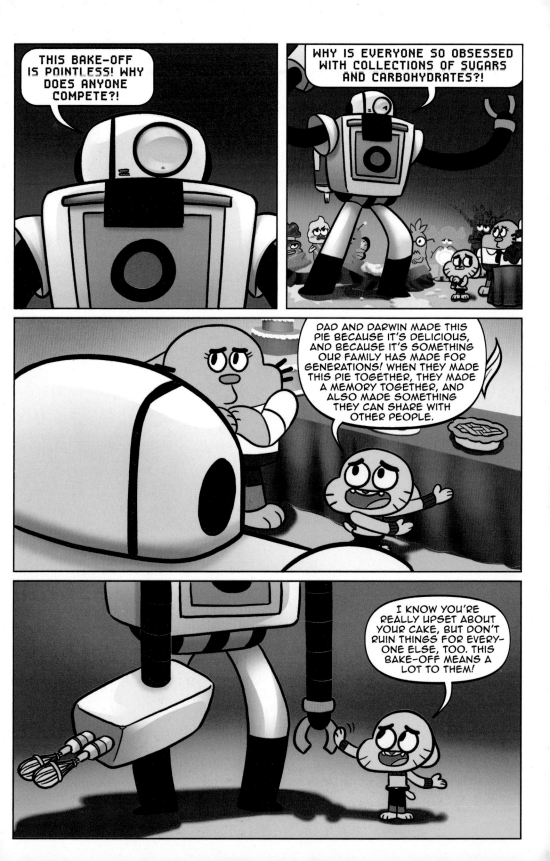

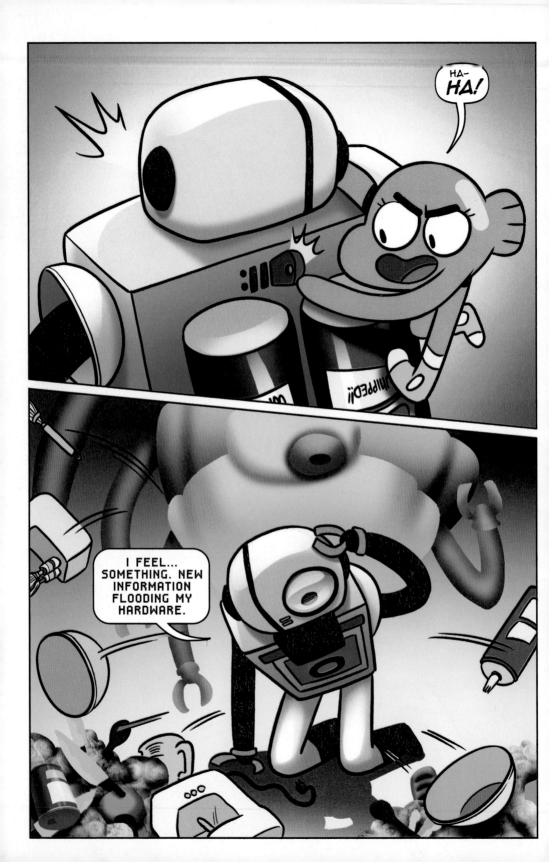

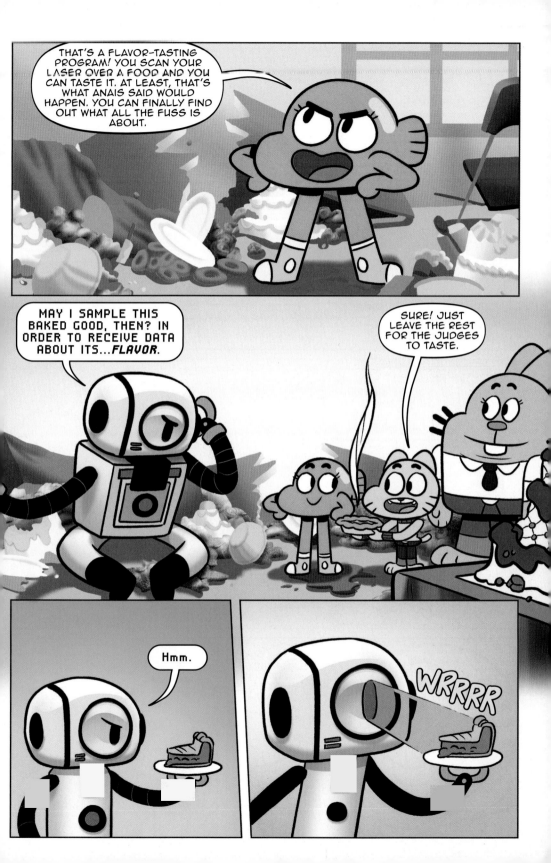

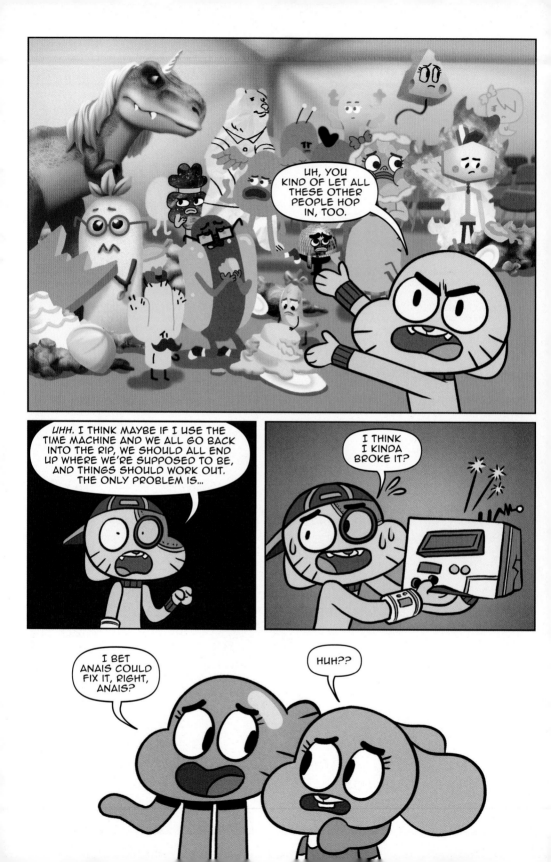

THOUGH THE COUNTY FAIR IS IN A MONTH OR TWO. WE COULD TRY TO GROW THE BIGGEST PUMPKIN IN ELMORE!

NO WAY!!

OR WHAT ABOUT THE ELMORE CRAFT FAIR? WE COULD LEARN A CRAFT!

WE COULD ENTER A BEAUTY PAGEANT!

BLIIIIP!

HEY, WHERE'D EVERYBODY GO ALL OF A SUDDEN? IS THE FOOD FIGHT OVER?

BAKE OFF 2DAY

OH WELL!

THE END!

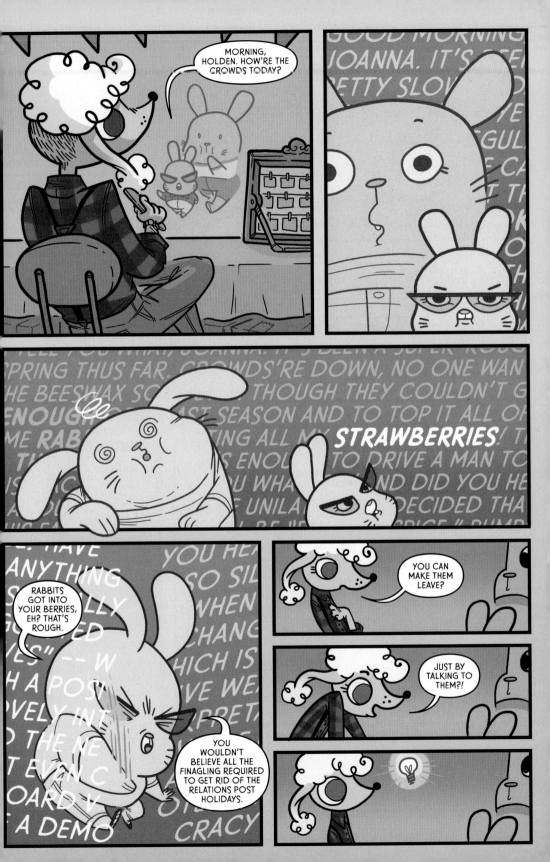

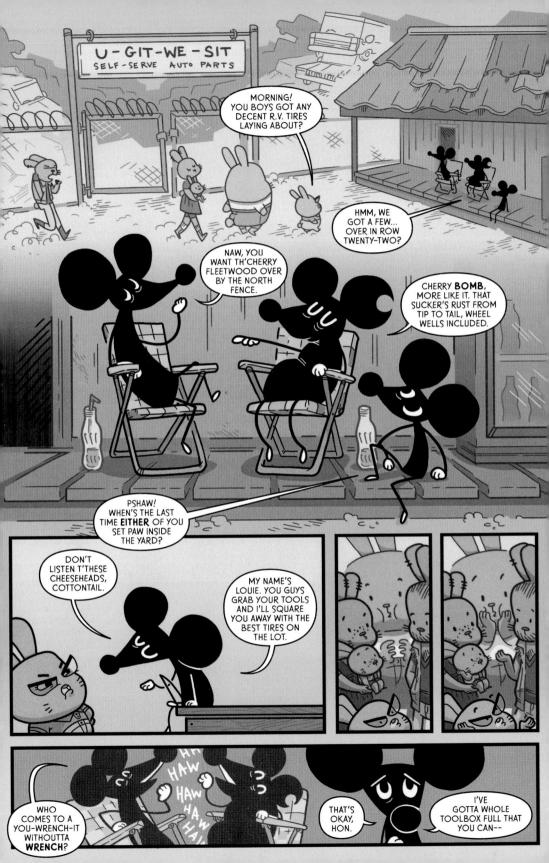

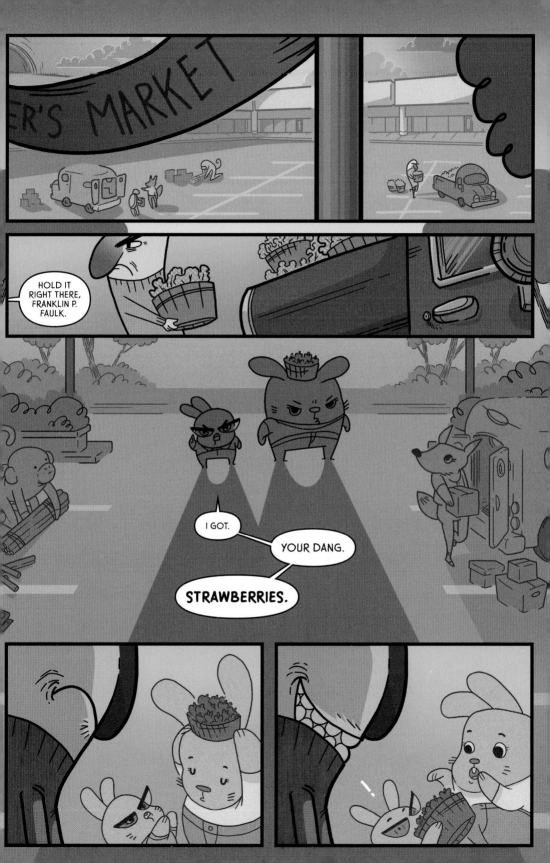

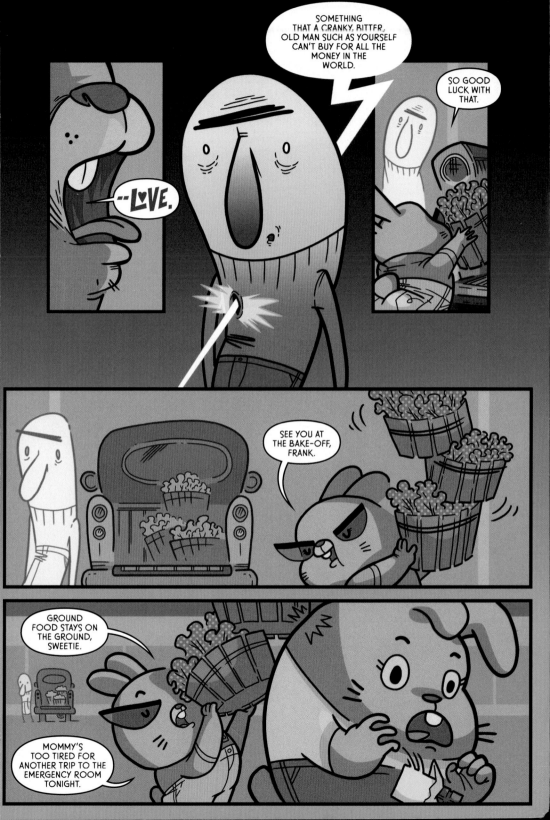

THE AMAZING WORLD OF GUMBALL

CONTINUES IN 2018